Fedya Ili

PORTUGUESE AZULEJOS

Coloring Book

for Relaxation, Meditation and Stress-Relief

FEDYA·BERLIN

2020

Relaxing and inspiring coloring book for grownups
with every skill level. 33 hand-drawn designs of
Portuguese facade ceramic tilework ornaments.
Stress-relieving patterns personally collected
and drawn by hand, original illustrations by artist
Fedya Ili (no stock images). Geometric repeat
patterns, florals, and abstract designs. Suitable for
coloring with markers, pencils, crayons, gel pens,
or watercolors. Explore your creativity and find
your inner balance.

FEDYA•BERLIN

CPSIA information can be obtained
at www.ICGtesting.com
Printed in the USA
LVHW060827240620
658653LV00021B/466